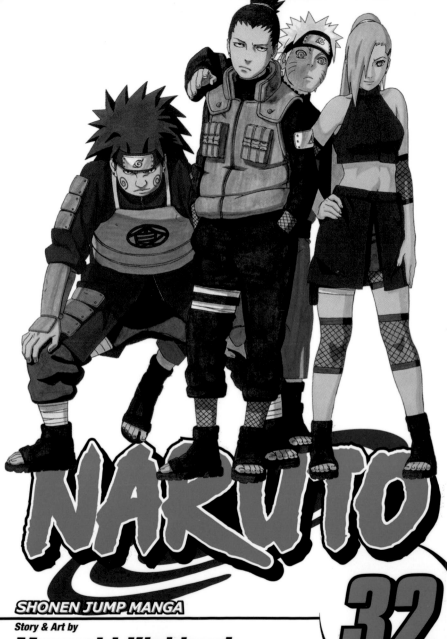

NARUTO

SHONEN JUMP MANGA

Story & Art by
Masashi Kishimoto   volume

32

岸本斉史

It's 2006. I believe the serialization began in 1999, so that means we've entered our seventh year of publication! Long enough for kids that were just entering elementary school to now be in junior high... I recently started noticing how it seems like the years pass quicker and quicker. Where in the world did the time go?! When in the world did I become middle-aged?! Yikes...

—*Masashi Kishimoto, 2006*

Author/artist Masashi Kishimoto was born in 1974 in rural Okayama Prefecture, Japan. After spending time in art college, he won the Hop Step Award for new manga artists with his manga **Karakuri** (Mechanism). Kishimoto decided to base his next story on traditional Japanese culture. His first version of **Naruto**, drawn in 1997, was a one-shot story about fox spirits; his final version, which debuted in **Weekly Shonen Jump** in 1999, quickly became the most popular ninja manga in Japan.

NARUTO VOL. 32
The SHONEN JUMP Manga Edition

This graphic novel contains material that was originally published in English in **SHONEN JUMP** #69-70. Artwork in the magazine may have been slightly altered from that presented here.

STORY AND ART BY MASASHI KISHIMOTO

Translation/Mari Morimoto
English Adaptation/Deric A. Hughes & Benjamin Raab
Touch-up Art & Lettering/Sabrina Heep
Design/Sean Lee
Editor/Joel Enos

Editor in Chief, Books/Alvin Lu
Editor in Chief, Magazines/Marc Weidenbaum
VP of Publishing Licensing/Rika Inouye
VP of Sales/Gonzalo Ferreyra
Sr. VP of Marketing/Liza Coppola
Publisher/Hyoe Narita

NARUTO © 1999 by Masashi Kishimoto. All rights reserved. First published in Japan in 1999 by SHUEISHA Inc., Tokyo. English translation rights arranged by SHUEISHA Inc. The stories, characters and incidents mentioned in this publication are entirely fictional.

The rights of the author(s) of the work(s) in this publication to be so identified have been asserted in accordance with Copyright, Designs and Patents Act 1988. A CIP catalogue record for this book is available from the British Library.

Printed in the U.S.A.

Published by VIZ Media, LLC
P.O. Box 77010
San Francisco, CA 94107

SHONEN JUMP Manga Edition
10 9 8 7 6 5 4 3 2 1
First printing, November 2008

THE WORLD'S
MOST POPULAR MANGA

www.viz.com

PARENTAL ADVISORY
NARUTO is rated T for Teen and is recommended for ages 13 and up. This volume contains realistic and fantasy violence.
ratings.viz.com

www.shonenjump.com

SHONEN JUMP MANGA EDITION

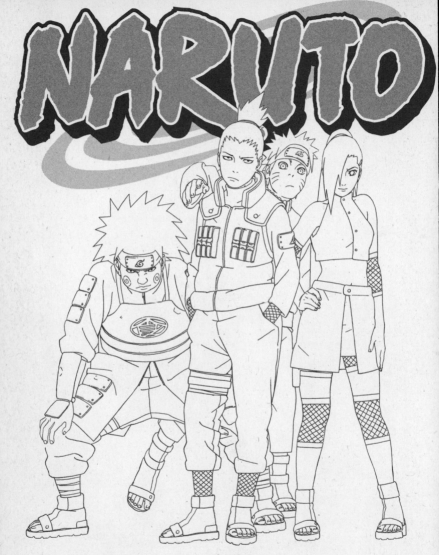

NARUTO

VOL. 32
THE SEARCH FOR SASUKE

STORY AND ART BY
MASASHI KISHIMOTO

Sakura
サクラ

Naruto
ナルト

Yamato
ヤマト

Sai サイ

Kakashi
カカシ

Danzo
ダンゾウ

Shizune
シズネ

Tsunade
綱手

Ino　いの

Choji チョウジ

Shikamaru
シカマル

The Story So Far...

Naruto, the biggest troublemaker at the Ninja Academy in Konohagakure, finally becomes a ninja along with his classmates Sasuke and Sakura. During the Chûnin Selection Exams, Orochimaru and his henchmen launch *Operation Destroy Konoha*. To stop the attack and prevent the deaths of any more of Konoha's shinobi, Sarutobi, the Third Hokage, sacrifices his own life. In the wake of this tragedy, Lady Tsunade is sought out and declared Fifth Hokage.

Sasuke—lured by the Sound Ninja Four of Orochimaru—leaves Konohagakure. Naruto fights valiantly against Sasuke, but cannot stop his friend from following the possible path of darkness...

After two years, Naruto and his comrades reunite, each having grown and matured in attitude and aptitude. Gaara of the Sand has become Kazekage, and falls into the hands of the mysterious organization known as the Akatsuki.

After several fierce battles, Naruto and the others defeat rogue ninja Sasori and Deidara and recover Gaara. But their victory looks to be a bitter one as Gaara is dead. Or so it seems until Granny Chiyo, using a reincarnation jutsu, sacrifices her own life to resurrect the fallen Kazekage!

NARUTO

VOL. 32
THE SEARCH FOR SASUKE

CONTENTS

NUMBER 281: THE SEARCH FOR SASUKE!! — 7

NUMBER 282: TEAM KAKASHI RETURNS — 29

NUMBER 283: TEAM MEMBERS WANTED!! — 49

NUMBER 284: THE NEW CELL...!! — 69

NUMBER 285: THE FOUNDATION — 89

NUMBER 286: NARUTO, SASUKE & SAKURA — 109

NUMBER 287: UNTITLED — 127

NUMBER 288: FEELINGS...? — 145

NUMBER 289: THE AKATSUKI SPY!! — 163

Number 281:
The Search for Sasuke!!

THEY'RE SCHEDULED TO RETURN TO KONOHA THREE DAYS FROM NOW.

TEAM GUY AND TEAM KAKASHI HAVE SUCCESSFULLY COMPLETED THEIR MISSIONS.

LORD KAZEKAGE HAS RETURNED SAFELY TO HIS VILLAGE.

SUFFERED JUST ONE CASUALTY... SUNA-GAKURE'S GRANNY CHIYO.

...

VERY WELL...

WHAT IS IT?

UM... LADY TSUNA-DE?

...

...INTO THE LAIR OF THE VERY PEOPLE TARGETING TAILED BEASTS...

...I STILL AGREE WITH LORD JIRAIYA THAT IT IS INADVISABLE TO INTENTION-ALLY SEND NARUTO...

EVEN THOUGH *THIS* MISSION WENT RELATIVELY WELL...

DESPITE THE FACT THAT FORMER BLACK OPS HATAKE KAKASHI IS HIS COMMANDER ...

...WHY CONTINUE TO TAKE SUCH GREAT AND DANGEROUS RISKS WITH HIM...?

BECAUSE HE'S A JINCHŪ-RIKI.

...ARE OTHER JINCHŪ-RIKI.

THE ONLY PEOPLE THAT TRULY UNDER-STAND JINCHŪ-RIKI...

?!

AND BESIDES...

...HE'S GOT THAT MYSTERIOUS POWER...

...ONE THAT MAKES EVERYONE... WANT TO BET ON HIM...

(HEADSTONE: CHIYO)

WHIRL...

SAKURA, YOU COMING?

RIGHT!

SAKURA, NARUTO, TIME TO GO.

THANK YOU... GRANNY CHIYO...

TCCH

WHISH

...

...

YEAH...

SO LONG...

!

...I'M NOT REALLY GOOD AT THESE THINGS, SO... LET'S JUST...

HEH... I GUESS THIS IS WHERE WE'RE SUPPOSED TO SHAKE HANDS OR SOMETHING, BUT...

...

SWISH SWISH

MASTERS, YOU'RE SO SLOW!

HEY!

WAIT!

OKAY, THEN!

THE MANGEKYO SHARINGAN TAKES A LOT OUT OF ME... GONNA BE A WHILE BEFORE I CAN MOVE ON MY OWN AGAIN...

SORRY, GUY.

...

BRILLIANT, MASTER GUY! A TRAINING DRILL!!

...

ERRR... WHAT?!

ARE THEY PLAYING PIGGYBACK? ...THAT'S JUST WEIRD...

UMM, WHAT ARE THEY DOING?

VOOOSH

A-HA HA HA! HOPE YOU ALL CAN KEEP UP WITH ME!!

OKAY, PEOPLE! NOW WE'RE MOVING !!

WHISH

! YOU THERE, DROP MY HAND!

I BET HE MET HIS DEMISE FROM *DEATH BY BOMBING...*

...ZETSU.

THERE ARE PROBABLY BODY PARTS SCATTERED ALL OVER THE AREA... HEH HEH...

WELL... MY TASTE BUDS DO BETRAY ME ...YOU'RE ALIVE!

HUF

HUF

I HAVE COMPLETED MY MISSION... HMMM?

WHAT HAPPENED TO THE JINCHŪRIKI?

...

BUT AT LEAST YOU'RE ALL RIGHT...

...OR PERHAPS NOT...

A CLOSE ONE THOUGH, EH, DEIDARA?

LEAP

DEATH BY SUFFOCATION...!

CLAMP

UGH!

TOBI, EVEN THE BUDDHA LOSES PATIENCE EVENTUALLY...

ONE MORE WORD, AND THERE'LL BE NO DOUBT ABOUT THE CAUSE OF YOUR DEATH... HMMM?

ULP! D-DEATH BY B-BOMBING...?

THERE... THAT'S IT.

HUP

I HAVE ALREADY MADE ARRANGEMENTS...

...FOR YOU TO BE ASSIGNED TO TEAM KAKASHI...

AND YOUR TALENT WITH THE BRUSH... IS SIMPLY UNSURPASSED.

...YOU'RE BOTH STRONGER THAN YOUR PEERS...

NOT ONLY ARE YOU AND UZUMAKI NARUTO CLOSE IN AGE...

JAB

...YOU SHALL BE KNOWN AS *SAI*...

FROM THIS DAY FORWARD, UNTIL YOUR MISSION IS COMPLETED...

WHEN YOU'RE IN FRONT OF ME, WIPE THAT FAKE SMILE OFF YOUR FACE.

...

FORGIVE ME, SIR... BUT IT WAS MENTIONED IN THE TEXTS THAT THE FIRST STEP TOWARD WINNING A PERSON'S HEART IS A *SMILE*...

I'VE BEEN PRACTIC-ING, BUT...

I GUESS I'M STILL NOT VERY GOOD...

...AT FACIAL EXPRES-SIONS...

UGH... AGAIN WITH THE BED REST...?

CAN YOU TRUST THE INFORMATION?

WHAT IF IT'S A TRAP?

(SIGNPOST: KONOHA HOSPITAL)

...

...TO LURE US TO THIS TENCHI BRIDGE...

...WHERE THEY'LL AMBUSH US...?

MAYBE THE AKATSUKI IS USING OROCHIMARU'S NAME AS BAIT...

火

30

...

IF IT *IS* A TRAP ...

...THEN WE FIGHT!

AND THERE ARE ONLY SIX DAYS LEFT UNTIL THE RENDEZ-VOUS...

...SO THE ONLY SOLUTION IS TO ASSEMBLE A NEW TEAM...

YES, BUT KAKASHI WILL BE OUT OF COMMISSION FOR OVER A WEEK NOW.

AND EVEN IF YOU DECIDE TO SEND SAKURA ALONG WITH THEM...

IN THAT CASE, WHY NOT JUST DEPLOY A DIFFERENT CELL?

WHAT IS IT?

LADY TSU-NADE ...

...I FEEL NARUTO SHOULD BE REMOVED FROM THIS MISSION ...!

...

...

THIS MISSION MUST INVOLVE THE REMAINING MEMBERS OF TEAM KAKASHI.

...SAKURA IS AMONG THE VERY FEW SHINOBI THAT I TRUST IMPLICITLY.

LIKE YOU, SHIZUNE ...

FRANKLY ...? NO.

YOU DON'T THINK MY CELL CAN HANDLE IT?

SASUKE IS NOT MERELY THEIR FORMER TEAMMATE. HE'S THEIR *FRIEND.*

IT'S *PERSONAL.*

THIS IS MORE THAN JUST A MISSION TO TEAM KAKASHI.

....?

...

...AND WHY YOU AND YOUR TEAM, SHIZUNE, MIGHT NOT.

THEY'VE PLEDGED THEIR LIVES TO RESCUING HIM. THEIR DESIRE TO HONOR THAT PLEDGE IS WHY THEY *WILL* SUCCEED...

?

WHAT DO YOU THINK *NARUTO*...

...WOULD SAY ABOUT THAT?

BUT I STILL THINK NARUTO...

UNDER-STOOD.

34

THUMP...

SEE YA!

I'M NOT FINISHED YET.

...SIGH ...SO IMPA- TIENT.

SHOOM

...THAT MAKES EVERY- ONE... WANT TO BET ON HIM...

...HE'S GOT A MYSTER- IOUS POWER...

...

35

...MAYBE NARUTO REALLY **IS** A SPECIAL CHILD...

SHE **DID** BESTOW ON HIM THE FIRST HOKAGE'S NECK-LACE...

TO BE HOKAGE IS MY DREAM...

...YES, MILADY...

SHF

PLEASE INFORM NARUTO.

WE WILL FILL THE TWO VACANCIES LEFT BY KAKASHI AND SASUKE.

TSUNADE...

!

36

...

COME WITH ME, PLEASE.

WE NEED TO TALK.

SHOOM

SASUKE!!

ACTUALLY...

...WE HAVE BEEN RECEIVING PERIODIC REPORTS FROM SHIZUNE.

...

IN ADDITION, ASSIGN TWO ACCOMPLISHED SHINOBI TO REMAIN AT HIS SIDE AT ALL TIMES.

NOT ONLY WILL THIS SERVE TO BETTER PROTECT HIM, BUT IT WILL RESTORE TEAM KAKASHI TO THE REQUISITE FOUR-MAN CELL.

HENCE-FORTH, UZUMAKI NARUTO...

...MUST NOT BE DISPATCHED ON MISSIONS THAT MIGHT BRING HIM INTO CONTACT WITH THE AKATSUKI.

...

...THE MORE LIMITED THE SCOPE OF HIS ACTIVITIES, THE BETTER.

AND DO TRY TO CUT BACK AS MUCH AS POSSIBLE HIS OVERALL NUMBER OF MISSIONS...

HMM, I WONDER WHO WOULD BE GOOD FOR THE JOB...?

CRUNCH

LIKE I SAID, *DO I KNOW YOU?*

IT'S ME!

FWIP

DO I... KNOW YOU?

?

LONG TIME NO SEE, NARUTO...

SHINO ?!

I KNOW THAT IRRITATING VOICE!

DON'T TELL ME...

...

FOOL, HOW AM I SUPPOSED TO RECOGNIZE YOU WITH YOUR FACE HIDDEN LIKE THAT?!

FINALLY ...YOU REMEM- BERED.

WHOM

!

MP

SHINO, YOU'RE EARLY!

RUSTLE...

NARUTO, IT WAS YOU, AFTER ALL!

HEY!

K... KIBA?

...

THAT'S WHAT YOU RECOGNIZED?!

...I THOUGHT I RECOGNIZED YOUR SCENT!

TAP

...

THAT DOG... HE CAN'T BE...

...

WOOF!!

COME ON!

OF COURSE IT'S AKAMARU!

I DIDN'T KNOW DOGS COULD GET THAT BIG SO FAST.

ME...? AKA-MARU'S THE ONE THAT GREW.

...

BUT HEY... DID YOU GROW OR SOME-THING?!

HE USED TO SIT ON TOP OF YOUR HEAD!

HOW COULD YOU NOT NOTICE?!

...REALLY?

HEH, GUESS I NEVER NOTICED BECAUSE HE'S ALWAYS WITH ME...

44

...NARUTO.

YOU RECOGNIZED KIBA RIGHT AWAY...

...

RIGHT, SHINO?

EEK!

...SHOOT ...NOW HE'S MAD AT ME...

...

...

!

OH DEAR... I'M NOT PREPARED...

I HEARD HE'D RETURNED, BUT...

I HAVEN'T SEEN HIM IN THREE YEARS, SO... WHAT DO I EVEN SAY TO HIM...? UM... UM...

W...WAS THAT REALLY NARUTO ...?!

...

ARE YOU HIDING OVER HERE?

OH, IT'S YOU, HINATA!

POP...

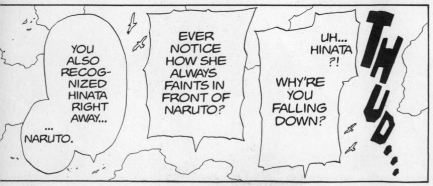

YOU ALSO RECOGNIZED HINATA RIGHT AWAY... ...NARUTO.

EVER NOTICE HOW SHE ALWAYS FAINTS IN FRONT OF NARUTO?

UH... HINATA ?!

WHY'RE YOU FALLING DOWN?

THUD...

WELL, THERE GO THOSE CHOICES...

TEAM KURENAI'S ALREADY ON ASSIGNMENT...

中忍試験
準備委員会

AT THIS RATE...

...THE ONLY ONES LEFT TO ASK ARE...

(SIGN: CHÛNIN EXAM PLANNING COMMITTEE)

IT'S A HUGE BOTHER, BUT I'M ON THE STAFF FOR THE CHÛNIN EXAM.

...I *TOLD* YOU...

AND AFTER MY MOM, THERE'S ONLY SO MUCH FEMALE SCOLDING I CAN TAKE.

...IT'S THE FIFTH HOKAGE'S ORDERS ...

...I'M NOT IN A POSITION WHERE I CAN JUST DO WHATEVER I LIKE.

YOU HAVE TO UNDER-STAND...

I MEAN... I KNOW WE GO WAY BACK...

...AND I REALLY DO WANT TO HELP YOU OUT, BUT...

THEN ALLOW *ME* TO PICK UP THE SLACK.

I THOUGHT YOU WERE ON ASSIGNMENT WITH MASTER ASUMA AND INO?

CHOJI...

...WHAT ARE YOU DOING HERE?

CHOJI!!

THANKS, CHOJI!!

I CAN ASK MASTER ASUMA FOR ADVICE.

YEAH, BUT I CAN'T JUST LEAVE NARUTO HANGING.

...LADY TSUNADE IS STILL HIS SUPERIOR...

I'M TELLING YOU...IT'S USELESS TO ASK ASUMA...

HEH HEH...
ALWAYS
EATING,
JUST LIKE
OLD TIMES.

KRUNCH
KRUNCH

DIDN'T
KNOW
IT WAS
POSSIBLE,
BUT IT
LOOKS LIKE
YOU'VE EVEN
GAINED
WEIGHT.

BOOF

HEY...!!

FL AP

HE CAME OUT OF NOWHERE... I DON'T KNOW WHAT HE WANTS...

...BUT SOMEONE LIKE THAT, YOU CAPTURE FIRST...

SKLORCH

...I DON'T RECOGNIZE HIM...BUT HE'S GOT A KONOHA HEADBAND!

scritch...

splish

...AND THEN HAND OVER TO THE TORTURE AND INTERROGATION CORPS!

swish swish swish swish

SPLASH

OK!

GO!

NARUTO, I'LL COVER YOU!

SHOOM!

THE ART OF CARTOON BEAST MIMICRY!!

FWIP

KEEP MOVING, NARUTO!

FWIP

THE ART OF SHADOW STITCH- ING!!

VOO

OSH

CLENCH

SWISH

KASHI

NK

YOU'RE... PRETTY WEAK.

ARE YOU A BOY OR A GIRL?

WHO... ARE YOU ...?!

6th ANNIVERSARY
CONGRATULATIONS

2005.11.8

田坂 亮
TASAKA RYÛ

Number 284: The New Cell...!!

ABSO-LUTELY NOT!

HE IS A JINCHÛ-RIKI.

TSU-NADE...

...NARUTO IS NO ORDINARY CHILD.

I'M IN FAVOR OF USING THE FOUR-MAN CELL MODEL FOR HIS TEAM, BUT YOU CANNOT IMPOSE ANY MORE RESTRICTIONS ON NARUTO!

...AND KEEP HIM UNDER SURVEILLANCE AT ALL TIMES.

NORMALLY, WE WOULD NEVER EVEN SEND HIM OUTSIDE THE VILLAGE...

SO WE'RE ALREADY OFFERING YOU A COMPRO-MISE.

70

...AND IT'LL BE SUNAGAKURE ALL OVER AGAIN... HOWEVER...

...A MOVING TARGET IS HARDEST TO HIT, WHICH IS WHY WE MUST KEEP NARUTO IN THE FIELD AS LONG AND AS OFTEN AS POSSIBLE.

SOONER OR LATER, THE AKATSUKI *WILL* COME FOR HIM...

SO LONG AS NARUTO REMAINS IN ONE PLACE, ALL OF KONOHA IS IN DANGER.

NARUTO *DOES* HAVE TALENT.

SOMEDAY HE WILL BE A GREAT ASSET TO KONOHA.

...

STOMP

SOMEDAY... THAT... IS YOUR ARGUMENT, TSUNADE?

AND YOU HAVE THE NERVE TO CALL YOURSELF HOKAGE?

LOOK! I'M TRYING TO COMPROMISE HERE, TOO!!

TELL ME, *LADY HOKAGE*... WHAT GUARANTEES CAN YOU GIVE...

...THAT SUCH A TRAGEDY WILL NEVER COME TO PASS?!

COMPROMISE...WILL NOT SPARE THE LIVES OF THE CITIZENS OF THIS VILLAGE...

...ONCE THE AKATSUKI HAVE EXTRACTED THE NINE TAILS FROM NARUTO.

IF YOU DIE... EVERYTHING...

...DREAMS AND EVERYTHING ELSE IS GONE!!

...THAT BAD LUCK NECKLACE AROUND YOUR NECK... I'M GONNA TAKE IT...

AS PROMISED IN OUR BET...

...

...IT'S OKAY...

...HEH...

RUN!

GET OUT OF THE WAY!!

A CHARM TO MAKE YOUR DREAM COME TRUE.

...THERE'S NO WAY I'M GONNA DIE!!

UNTIL I BECOME HOKAGE...

73

I BELIEVE IN HIM.

NARUTO ...WILL NOT FALL!

...

AND IF YOU ARE MISTAKEN ...?

WHAT THEN?

...

...AND SUBSE-QUENTLY THE LAND OF FIRE, ARE ENDANGERED BECAUSE OF ME...

IF... KONOHA-GAKURE ...

THEN I SWEAR, AS THE FIFTH HOKAGE, TO PROTECT THEM WITH ALL MY MIGHT.

AND MY VERY OWN LIFE...

...

...

...

...WHO ARE TO JOIN TEAM KAKASHI.

...WE SHALL SELECT THE ADDITIONAL SHINOBI...

TO HONOR YOUR FAITH IN HIM, NARUTO SHALL BE ALLOWED TO REMAIN IN ACTIVE DUTY... HOWEVER...

AS YOU WISH, THEN...A COMPROMISE...

...ENTER! DANZO...

DONE.

...

SWISH

!

CLATTER

... DANZO ...

HELLO, PRINCESS. BEEN A LONG TIME...

...THEN THAT MUST MEAN ONE OF THE NEW TEAM MEMBERS ...

IF YOU'RE HERE...

78

LEAP

IN DUE TIME, NARUTO. ALL IN DUE TIME...

HEY, WAIT!!

SWIRL

! CHOJI! HOW'D I KNOW I'D FIND YOU HERE...?!

WHO WAS THAT GUY...?

...

...

SOME WEIRDO JUST SUDDENLY ATTACKED US...

SORRY, INO...

...

WEIRDO?

SAVE YOUR BREATH, CHOJI. IT'S SO NOT WORTH IT...

HEY, NARUTO!! LONG TIME NO SEE!

NO, NO... NOT HIM...! UHH...

WHO? NARUTO ...?

THEY WILL HAVE TO LEAVE BEFORE KAKASHI FINISHES RECU-PERATING...

...TEAM KAKASHI WILL NEED ONE MORE MEMBER.

...THEN THE CHOICE IS CLEAR...YOU REQUIRE AN EXCEPTIONALLY DISTINGUISHED COMMANDER...

...ONE FROM AMONG THE BLACK OPS, ASSIGNED DIRECTLY TO THE HOKAGE HERSELF.

AND THERE'S NOT MUCH TIME BETWEEN NOW AND THEN.

YOU DON'T HAVE ANY OBJECTION TO *THAT*, DO YOU, TSUNADE?

YES!

THAT IS ACCEPT-ABLE.

...THAT'S WHY I NEED YOU TO FILL IN FOR YOUR PREDECESSOR.

...AND SO...

...

GLANCE

I AM GREATLY HONORED.

MASTER KAKASHI...? THOSE ARE HUGE SHOES TO FILL.

CLOP

WHILE ON THIS MISSION, YOU WILL CALL YOURSELF YAMATO.

THERE-FORE, YOU MUST REMOVE YOUR MASK...

...AND BE ASSIGNED A CODE NAME.

UNDER-STAND THIS WILL NOT BE A BLACK OPS MISSION...

...BUT A REGULAR MISSION.

UNDER-STOOD.

YOU MUST...

YES?

...A NEW FACE FROM *THE FOUNDATION*, THE BLACK OPS TRAINING DIVISION...

...IS ALSO ASSIGNED TO TEAM KAKASHI.

...THERE'S ONE OTHER THING...

...AND ...THE REASON FOR THIS?

...KEEP A CLOSE EYE ON HIM.

AND DANZO...

...IS NOT ONLY A MEMBER OF THE HAWK FACTION THAT ONCE OPPOSED THE THIRD HOKAGE...

DANZO SELECTED THIS NEW-COMER.

THOUGH THE FOUNDATION HAS SINCE BEEN DISSOLVED, AND DANZO REMOVED...

...I CAN'T HELP BUT BE SUSPICIOUS OF HIS MOTIVES.

...BUT ALSO THE FOUNDER OF A SEPARATE DETAIL WITHIN THE BLACK OPS...

...A TRAINING DIVISION KNOWN AS *THE FOUNDATION.*

SURELY YOU'VE HEARD OF HIM...

PERHAPS... BUT NO MATTER...

GO. JOIN YOUR NEW CELL.

YES, MA'AM!

...

NO DISRESPECT, MILADY... BUT MIGHT YOU BE OVERREACTING...?

Y— YOU!!

HELLO AGAIN ...

SO... UM... STARTING TODAY...

...I'LL BE FILLING IN FOR KAKASHI...

...

!

...AND WHETHER OR NOT I'D EVENTUALLY HAVE TO COME TO THE LITTLE BOY'S AID.

 I WAS JUST CURIOUS TO SEE HOW STRONG MY FUTURE TEAMMATE MIGHT BE...

SORRY ABOUT OUR EARLIER ENCOUNTER.

NARUTO, YOU KNOW THIS GUY?

 REALLY?

BUT I LIKE UGLY GIRLS LIKE YOU.

 ...THAT WASN'T VERY NICE...

...AND YOU...

 HEY! WE HAVE TO WORK TOGETHER! SO DON'T FIGHT RIGHT FROM THE GET-GO!

WHAT ?!

 WHOA! EASY, SAKURA! FOLLOW YOUR OWN ADVICE!

WHAT DID YOU JUST SAY?!

Happy 6th
Anniversary 2005'

printed by 西谷浩一,
NISHIYA KÚICHI

...SO, UM...WHY DON'T YOU GUYS GO AHEAD...

...WE REALLY DON'T HAVE TIME TO SOCIAL-IZE.

...AND INTRO-DUCE YOUR-SELVES.

ANYWAY...

...SINCE WE'RE GOING TO BE DEPLOYING ALMOST IMMEDIATELY...

I AM SAI.

I'M HARUNO SAKURA.

UZUMAKI NARUTO.

...LET ME EXPLAIN OUR MISSION.

ALL RIGHT, NOW THAT THAT'S OVER WITH...

THE FOUR OF US WILL HEAD TO TENCHI BRIDGE...

...CAPTURE THE AKATSUKI SPY WHO HAS INFILTRATED OROCHIMARU'S ORGANIZATION, AND BRING HIM OR HER BACK HERE.

...TO GAIN INTELLIGENCE ON OROCHIMARU AND UCHIHA SASUKE...

THIS IS OUR BEST CHANCE...

SO KEEP THAT IN MIND!

...AND SASUKE'S RETRIEVAL.

...INFORMATION WE CAN THEN USE TO PLAN OROCHIMARU'S ASSASSINATION...

THEN WE'LL DEPART!

...RENDEZ-VOUS AT THE MAIN GATE.

AS SOON AS EVERYONE'S GEAR IS ALL PACKED...

THAT JERK SAI... I ALREADY CAN'T STAND HIM!

HIS FACE... HIS VOICE... THEY KIND OF REMIND ME OF SASUKE...

HE IS RUDE... AND HE'S GOT A FOUL MOUTH...BUT... THERE IS SOMETHING FAMILIAR ABOUT HIM.

...

TEAM KAKASHI IS FINE WITH JUST THE THREE OF US!

WHY DOES *HE* HAVE TO BE SASUKE'S REPLACE-MENT...?

...I MEAN...!

SASUKE'S WAY COOLER...!

NOT AT ALL!

SASUKE'S A BAZILLION TIMES BETTER!!

MORE THAN JUST A LITTLE!

YOU'RE RIGHT. SASUKE IS A LITTLE COOLER THAN SAI.

...

KACHI

NG!

...

BUT REMEMBER... NEVER LET YOUR GUARD DOWN.

...VERY NICE REFLEXES.

WHAT DO YOU WANT... SIR?

...YOUR TOP-SECRET MISSION.

FROM LORD DANZO...

FFT

...

GLANCE

FLIP

!!

...IS DIRECTED BY LORD DANZO. THE FUTURE OF KONOHA DEPENDS UPON YOUR SUCCESS.

LISTEN, THIS SECRET MISSION YOU ARE ON...

MROWR!

ZWHAP

WHAM

...JUST A CAT...

HOOSH

... MISTAKES WILL NOT BE TOLERATED.

...IN ANY CASE...

...

I UNDER-STAND.

!

... THIS IS...

YOU...

...STILL CARRY THAT THING ...?

...HAVE NO NAMES...

...NO EMOTIONS ...

THOSE OF THE FOUN-DATION...

THERE IS **ONLY** THE MISSION...

...NO PAST...

...AND NO FUTURE...

NEVER FORGET THAT.

WE ARE THE ROOTS THAT SUPPORT...

...THE GREAT TRUNK OF KONOHA, INVISIBLE, FROM INSIDE THE EARTH...

...

YES, SIR.

...

SO...IT'S THAT BAD ALREADY, EH...

I'M AFRAID SO, MILADY...

I PROMISE I WILL TRY, BUT...

WELL, IF IT CAN'T BE HELPED...

...THEN YOU'LL PROBABLY HAVE TO KEEP NARUTO ON AN EVEN SHORTER LEASH THAN USUAL.

ENTER!

...

KNOCK KNOCK

101

DANZO
...

WHAT
IS IT?

WHO'S
HE?

...

102

I HAVE SELECTED AN EXEMPLARY SHINOBI...

...WITH EXPERIENCE FROM AS FAR BACK AS THE THIRD HOKAGE'S RULE.

...PRINCESS TSUNADE?

WERE YOU ABLE TO ASSIGN...

...A DISTINGUISHED BLACK OPS OPERATIVE TO LEAD SAI'S CELL...

....?

I JUST HOPE... HE'S NOT ROOTED TOO DEEPLY IN THE...

...PACIFIST TEACHINGS OF THAT PUSHOVER, SARUTOBI...

...VERY WELL...

JUST AS THE THIRD HOKAGE WAS ROOTED...

...IN THE TEACHINGS OF YOUR GRANDFATHER.

...HUMPH.

CLUNK...

...PRIN-CESS...

NOW, IF YOU'LL EXCUSE ME...

IN ANY CASE, I AM RELIEVED.

WHIRL

SOMEONE WHO, LONG AGO, COMPETED WITH THE LATE MASTER SARUTOBI...

...OVER THE SEAT OF THIRD HOKAGE.

THUMP

THUMP

...

THAT...?

UM, WHO WAS...

AS A STUDENT OF THE MODERATE THIRD HOKAGE...

...AND GRAND-DAUGHTER OF THE FIRST HOKAGE, HE ACTIVELY DESPISES ME.

...AND HE'S THE LEADER OF A HARD-LINE MARTIAL FACTION FOUNDED ON RIGID PRINCIPLES...

...HE'S ALSO SAI'S SUPERIOR.

HIS NAME IS DANZO...

THUMP

YES, MA'AM...

...TIME TO GO...

IT'S BEEN ALMOST AN HOUR, SAKURA...

...

NARUTO
6th Anniversary!!

'05, 11, 8 大久保彰
OHKUBO AKIRA

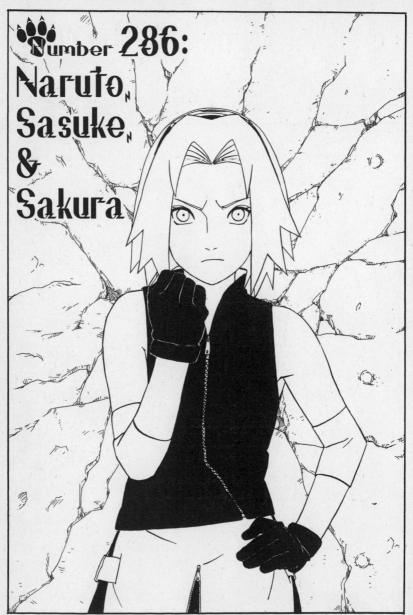

Number 286:
Naruto, Sasuke & Sakura

WHAT?

...

...SORTA SOUNDS LIKE HIM TOO...

FUNNY, BUT THE MORE I LOOK AT HIM, THE MORE HE *DOES* KINDA RESEMBLE SASUKE...

....!

I TAKE IT BACK. HE IS SOOOO *NOT* SASUKE!

WHAT? YOU THINK I'M SCARED OF YOU?

GRR

I WILL HIT YOU.

IF YOU KEEP LOOKING AT ME...

WELL... YOU'RE SURE DOING A CRUMMY JOB!

I'M JUST TRYING OUT...

...A CERTAIN PERSONALITY TYPE.

YEAH, RIGHT...

LOOK, I REALLY DON'T HAVE ANYTHING PERSONAL AGAINST YOU.

IN FACT, I BET WE'D BE A LOT BETTER OFF WITHOUT YOU... JERK!

WE DON'T NEED SOMEONE LIKE YOU ON THIS TEAM!

I KNOW KAKASHI-SENSEI TAUGHT YOU BETTER THAN THIS.

...YOU'RE STILL GOING TO HAVE TO FIND A WAY TO *TRUST* EACH OTHER.

SAI IS YOUR *TEAM-MATE* NOW...

...SO EVEN IF YOU DON'T GET ALONG...

THAT'S ENOUGH, NARUTO!

NO! HE'S NOT ONE OF US!

...LOSE THE ATTITUDE, HUH?

SO, PLEASE, FOR KAKASHI'S SAKE...

...IS UCHIHA SASUKE!!

THE FOURTH MEMBER OF TEAM KAKASHI...

...IS A SASUKE WANNABE!

HE WILL *NEVER* BE OUR TEAM-MATE.

...ALL THIS LOSER IS...

...ALL HE COULD EVER HOPE TO BE...

EVEN ON HIS BEST DAY...

...

...

FINE BY ME.

...

SMIRK

...WHO ABANDONED HIS VILLAGE FOR OROCHIMARU JUST BECAUSE...

...HE WANTED TO BECOME STRONGER...

THE LAST PERSON I'D EVER WANT TO BE COMPARED TO...

...IS SOME TRAITOROUS COCKROACH...

CLENCH

CRUNCH

HOW DARE YOU...

REGARDLESS OF EITHER OF YOUR OPINIONS...

!

BLOCK

BUT THAT'S NO EXCUSE FOR HIM TO JUDGE YOU.

NARUTO DOESN'T KNOW YOU ALL THAT WELL YET.

S... SAKURA...

PLEASE FORGIVE NARUTO.

I'M SORRY.

REALLY...?

...OH, GOOD.

HEY, LIKE I SAID... FINE BY ME.

GOOD TO SEE THERE'S AT LEAST ONE LEVELHEADED PERSON ON THIS TEAM.

WHEW...

...

?!

HUH ?!

I DON'T CARE...

...IF YOU FORGIVE ME.

NEVER SPEAK AS IF YOU DO!

YOU DON'T KNOW SASUKE...

AH...

YOUR SMILE WAS A *FAKE*...

JUST KEEP BAD-MOUTHING SASUKE...

...NEXT TIME I WON'T HOLD BACK...

...

...I'LL HAVE TO REMEMBER THAT.

...BUT, THAT CLEVER USE OF A FAKE SMILE...

HO HO... OKAY...I'LL KEEP MY MOUTH SHUT...

"...IT WILL FOOL MORE PEOPLE THAN YOU THINK."

...OR SO I'VE READ.

"THE BEST WAY TO DEFUSE A TROUBLESOME SITUATION IS BY SMILING...

"...EVEN IF IT IS A FAKE SMILE...

HOW STUPID ARE YOU?!

WHAT ARE YOU TALKING ABOUT?!

...

...

THOUGH IT NEVER SEEMS TO WORK FOR ME.

CROUCH

SPR OK

CRACK CRACK

FOUR-PILLAR PRISON TECHNIQUE!!

SLAM

KEEP IT UP, YOU THREE... AND I'LL THROW YOU *ALL* IN A CAGE!

WE ONLY HAVE FIVE DAYS TO GET TO TENCHI BRIDGE.

TH... THAT'S...

WOOD-STYLE NINJUTSU!!

...

...!

WHO *IS* HE...?

...

...SO HOW DOES COMMANDER YAMATO KNOW IT...?

...A SECRET JUTSU KNOWN ONLY TO THE FIRST HOKAGE ...!

...OR ENJOY A NIGHT AT A COMFORTABLE INN WITH A RELAXING HOT SPRING.

SPEND THE REST OF THE DAY CRAMMED INSIDE A WOODEN BOX REACQUAINTING YOURSELVES WITH THE MEANING OF TEAMWORK...

TWO CHOICES.

NOW, I'LL GIVE YOU...

...NOT AGAINST USING MORE DRACONIAN METHODS WHEN NECESSARY...

I PREFER THE KIND AND GENTLE APPROACH, BUT I'M...

LOO——M

YOU DON'T REALLY KNOW ME EITHER...

LOOM

DON'T YOU MEN THINK?

...NOW, THIS IS A MUCH BETTER WAY TO GET TO KNOW EACH OTHER!

AAH...

...

...

HUH, FANCY THAT...

NARUTO IS A BOY AFTER ALL.

...

COMMANDER YAMATO IS A TOTAL WEIRDO!

IN A HOT SPRING?! IF YOU SAY SO!

SPLASH

....!

I AM NOT COMFORT-ABLE IN THIS SETTING AT ALL!

OKAY, FIRST OF ALL...!

TEE-HEE-HEE-HEE-HEE-HEE

COME ON, NARUTO... LOWER YOUR VOICE, WILL YOU?!

TEE-HEE HEE HEE HEE!

...HAVING FRACTURED SIX RIBS AND BOTH ARMS AND SUFFERED RUPTURED INTERNAL ORGANS.

A VERY LONG TIME AGO, WHEN HE WAS JUST A BOY, YOUR MENTOR LORD JIRAIYA CAME THIS CLOSE TO DEATH...

...BUT BEFORE I GO, LET ME SHARE A FUNNY STORY WITH YOU, NARUTO.

WELL, THAT'S ENOUGH BONDING FOR ME...

SNEAK

SO BEFORE YOU HOP OUT OF THAT SPRING...

...I SUGGEST YOU STOP AND THINK...

THE REASON? SUPPOSEDLY... LADY TSUNADE FOUND OUT THAT HE DID...

...PRECISELY WHAT YOU'RE CONTEMPLATING RIGHT ABOUT NOW.

Number 287: Untitled

NOTHING LIKE A GOOD NIGHT'S SLEEP!

мммм ...!

...

SAI?

SCRTCH
SCRTCH

....!

...FOR THE ARTISTIC TYPE.

NEVER FIGURED YOU...

...

...

LOOKS CAN BE DECEIVING.

DON'T TELL ME YOU'RE...

...GONNA SLUG ME NOW?

THAT FAKE SMILE AGAIN...

DON'T I KNOW IT. Y'KNOW, FOR SOMEONE SO ROUGH ON THE OUTSIDE...

...YOU SEEM PRETTY SENSITIVE ON THE INSIDE.

I'LL TRY NOT TO.

SO... WHAT ARE YOU SKETCHING?

I'M ONLY PLAYING WITH YOU.

ONLY IF YOU GIVE ME A REASON.

...BUT THIS IS AN *ABSTRACT*.

I WOULD'VE THOUGHT THAT A PLACE LIKE THIS WOULD HAVE YOU DRAWING A LAND-SCAPE...

...DON'T KNOW...

IT'S STILL NICE...

WHAT ARE YOU CALLING IT?

YOU DON'T HAVE A TITLE FOR IT YET?

THERE IS NO TITLE...

HUH...

...BUT I'VE NEVER TITLED ANY OF THEM.

...I MEAN, I'VE DRAWN THOUSANDS, IF NOT TENS OF THOUSANDS, OF SKETCHES OVER TIME...

...TO CONVEY THE THOUGHTS, FEELINGS AND EMOTIONS...

...THEY FELT AND EXPERIENCED WHILE CREATING THE PIECE...

EVEN IF IT'S JUST SOMETHING SIMPLE...

I THOUGHT ALL ARTISTS NAMED THEIR WORK...?

...HONESTLY, WHENEVER I TRY TO GIVE THEM TITLES...

...NOTHING GOOD COMES TO MIND.

...

SCRITCH

...AND I JUST DON'T FEEL... *ANY-THING.*

THE RIGHT WORDS... ESCAPE ME...

?

...IS THAT WHY YOU'RE SUCH AN INSENSITIVE JERK...?

OK.

SO, IF YOU WOULDN'T MIND...

COMMANDER YAMATO SAYS IT'S TIME TO GO.

HUMPH! THAT DRAWING...

...IS NOTHING SPECIAL.

PEEK...

I **HATE** YOU!!

THAT'S IT! I'VE HAD IT!

JUST LIKE YOU.

SURE.

UGH...

...

JUST SAY IT!

IF YOU'VE GOT A PROBLEM WITH ME, DON'T GIVE ME THAT FAKE SMILE!

...

AND I'LL FIGHT YOU ANY-TIME!!

135

?!

BUT I DON'T HATE YOU, NARUTO ...

AS A MATTER OF FACT, I DON'T FEEL ANYTHING TOWARD YOU AT ALL, GOOD OR BAD.

...

...

I'LL HELP.

...

I'LL CATCH UP AS SOON AS I'VE PACKED.

PLEASE. JUST GO ON AHEAD.

FSH

!

...THIS ...IT'S NOT A PRINTED COPY.

DID YOU DRAW THIS, TOO?

!

HUMPH!

WOW...

...YOUR VERY OWN PICTURE BOOK...

YEAH...

SHF

...IT'S NOT FINISHED YET.

SORRY, BUT NO.

HEY...

...WHILE WE'RE ON THE ROAD, IS IT OKAY IF I FLIP THROUGH THIS?

!

?

PLUS, I DON'T REALLY SHOW IT TO OTHERS...

...BECAUSE IT BELONGS TO MY OLDER BROTHER.

....?

...

...

MOKUTON SHICHUKA NO JUTSU! WOOD STYLE FOUR-PILLAR HOUSE TECHNIQUE!!

THIS SPOT SHOULD DO NICELY...

...

WHA!

SPROCK SPROCK

DOOM

WE'LL CAMP OUT HERE TONIGHT.

UM... I DON'T THINK THIS REALLY QUALIFIES AS CAMPING OUT.

ALL RIGHT, GATHER AROUND, EVERYONE.

...THERE ARE A FEW THINGS I ESPECIALLY NEED TO ASK YOU.

OH, AND SAKURA...

! CLATTER

...WITH REGARD TO THE AKATSUKI MEMBER SASORI.

WHAT ABOUT?

AFTER ALL, YOU'RE THE ONLY ONE HERE...

...WHO'S GONE TOE-TO-TOE WITH HIM.

...IT WOULD BE HELPFUL IF YOU COULD FILL IN ANY BLANKS...

...ABOUT HIS PERSONALITY, SPEECH PATTERNS, MANNERISMS, OR QUIRKS...

I RECEIVED HIS FILE FROM SUNA-GAKURE, BUT...

THEY MIGHT CATCH ME RIGHT AWAY...

...BUT I'M GOING TO TRY TO APPROACH THEM DISGUISED AS SASORI.

THE AKATSUKI SPY WHO HAS INFILTRATED OROCHIMARU'S RANKS...

...EXPECTS TO RENDEZVOUS WITH SASORI AT TENCHI BRIDGE.

WHAT DO YOU NEED TO KNOW ALL THAT FOR?

YOU THREE WILL LIE IN WAIT UNTIL I SIGNAL YOU.

TRUE...AND SINCE THERE'S STILL A SMALL CHANCE THIS IS AN AKATSUKI TRAP... I'VE PLANNED FOR THAT POSSIBILITY AS WELL.

THAT'S WHY I'LL APPROACH FIRST, ALONE.

...YOUR TARGET WILL DEFINITELY HAVE THEIR GUARD UP.

SPY WORK ENTAILS PRETTY HIGH RISK, SO...

EITHER WAY, THIS SPY... IS MOST LIKELY QUITE STRONG AND ACCOMPLISHED...

...AND THE WAY SASORI MENTIONED IT, JUST BEFORE HE DIED...

...I DON'T THINK IT'S A LIE, BUT...

THERE **WAS** AN AKATSUKI SPY, YURA, IN THE SAND VILLAGE AS WELL...

YEAH, WELL... SO ARE WE...

FWHOO

MURAKAMI MASAKI

Number 288: Feel-ings...?

CRUNCH

...SO HERE'S THE MISSION FROM A TO Z...

THE DEVIL IS IN THE DETAILS, TEAM...

OUR ONE AND ONLY GOAL IS A *LIVE CAPTURE*...

EVEN IF IT MEANS HAVING TO FIGHT THEM.

...THE TARGET MUST *NOT* BE KILLED OR INJURED, NO MATTER WHAT.

SO... WHILE YOU THREE ACT AS BACKUP...

AND BECAUSE IT'S SUCH A DELICATE SITUATION...

...THIS MUST GO OFF WITHOUT A HITCH.

THEREFORE, THIS MISSION IS EVEN HARDER THAN WHEN YOU JUST HAVE TO TAKE DOWN THE ENEMY.

IF THEY'RE KILLED, WE LOSE OUR ONLY SOURCE OF INTELLIGENCE.

THEN, AND ONLY THEN, DO YOU SHIFT TO COMBAT MODE...

...ENTERING THE FRAY ON MY SIGNAL ALONE.

...AND IT IS REVEALED THAT I AM, IN FACT, *NOT* SASORI...

...A BATTLE WILL LIKELY ENSUE.

IF, BY SOME CHANCE, MY DISGUISE IS PENETRATED...

...I'LL GO AHEAD AND TRY TO CAPTURE THE TARGET BY MYSELF.

SO... HERE ARE THE PAIRINGS.

EVERY WARRIOR'S ACTION WILL BE COVERED BY THEIR PARTNER.

THE WATCH-WORD, PEOPLE, IS *TEAM-WORK.*

WE WILL FIGHT IN PAIRS AT ALL TIMES.

SQUAD ONE WILL BE... NARUTO AND SAI.

SAKURA, YOU'RE WITH ME...

148

YOU'RE THE TEAM'S ONE AND ONLY MEDIC NINJA.

BUT...

WE CAN'T AFFORD TO HAVE YOU INJURED, SO I WILL COVER YOU.

PART-NER.

!

...

OH, C'MON, COMMANDER!

TEAM ME UP WITH ANYONE... JUST NOT HIM!

...

AND YET YOU CONTINUE TO COMPLAIN...

LOO—M

!

I NEED TO ASSESS FIRSTHAND YOUR BATTLE STYLE AND SKILLS...

...THE MAKEUP OF YOUR JUTSU, ET CETERA.

EVERYTHING I KNOW ABOUT YOU THREE COMES FROM YOUR FILES.

...THIS ISN'T STANDARD PROCEDURE, BUT HALF OF TOMORROW...

...WILL BE FOCUSED ON PAIR SIMULATION EXERCISES.

...IN LIGHT OF WHAT I JUST TOLD YOU...

KAKASHI-SENSEI MAY HAVE FAVORED A MORE *LAX* APPROACH...

...BUT I AM NOT HE.

CLEARLY, IT'S THE ONLY WAY I'M EVER GOING TO FORGE THIS TEAM...

...INTO THE COHESIVE FIGHTING UNIT IT NEEDS TO BE.

150

SHOOM

WHUP WHUP WHUP

IS THAT ALL YOU'VE GOT?!

DUCK

THINK

WHIS

THE ART OF CARTOON BEAST MIMICRY!!

UNNH...!

TWITCH

GOTCHA! AND I'M NOT LETTING GO!!

SLITH

ERR!

HISSSS

154

(HEADGEAR: LOSER!)

...WE'LL END THE SIMU-LATIONS HERE.

NICE CATCH... SAI...

!

GRAB

CRUNCH

YOU KNOW WHAT THE WORD *COMRADE* MEANS?

PROB-LEM?

SCRIBBLE

SCRIBBLE

RUM-MAGE

AS A MATTER OF FACT...

SWISH

仲間

...I DO.

(ROLL: COMRADE)

...FOR YOUR OWN SHORT-COMINGS.

SERIOUSLY... DON'T GO BLAMING OTHERS...

...N-NARUTO, WAIT.

GNASH

IS THAT ALL YOU'VE GOT?!

EVEN IF YOU HAD USED YOUR OWN JUTSU AND TRANSFORMED INTO ME, HE STILL WOULD HAVE KNOWN IT WAS ONLY A SHADOW DOPPELGANGER.

...HE WOULDN'T HAVE KNOWN THAT I WAS HIDING ELSEWHERE.

IF YOU HADN'T FALLEN FOR THE COMMANDER'S OBVIOUS BAIT...

I SIMPLY CONSIDERED WHAT WOULD BEST ENSURE MISSION SUCCESS AND ACTED ACCORDINGLY.

IT'S IMPRACTICAL TO FIGHT WHILE COVERING FOR SOMEONE WHO CAN'T MAINTAIN HIS COOL... NOT TO MENTION DANGEROUS.

...

...WILL *NEVER* ACCEPT YOU AS A COMRADE...

...OR AS A MEMBER OF THIS TEAM!

I...

FWIP

WOULD *HE* HAVE FOUGHT WHILE COVERING YOU?

...I WONDER WHAT SASUKE WOULD HAVE DONE IN THIS SCENARIO?

SOME-HOW I DOUBT IT.

THIS IS SO NOT GOING TO WORK...

HUF

OH, SAI... WHY DO YOU INSIST ON PUSHING NARUTO?!

...

SWOSH

HE BETRAYED OUR VILLAGE AND TRIED TO *KILL* YOU.

AND YOU STILL CONSIDER HIM A COMRADE?

EVEN TEAM UP WITH YOU.

YES... AND I WOULD STILL DO **ANY- THING** TO SAVE HIM.

WHIRL

...

...

NARUTO...

...

...THINKS OF SASUKE AS A BROTHER.

N A R U T O...

...

THIS OBSESSION WITH SASUKE...

...IT'S ABSURD...

NO.

YOU HAVE AN OLDER BROTHER...

...SO YOU MUST KNOW WHAT THAT'S LIKE.

...

...I DON'T *HAVE* FEELINGS.

REMEMBER OUR CONVERSATION ABOUT THE PICTURE TITLES?

The Akatsuki Spy!!

HE'S YOUR **BROTHER.** SURELY YOU MUST FEEL **SOMETHING** ...

WHAT DO YOU MEAN YOU DON'T **HAVE** FEELINGS?

...

I MEAN EXACTLY WHAT I SAID.

...

...

SCRAPE

CLENCH

GRRRR

...

AH,
WELL...
YOU
SEE...

H
M
M
?

...YOU MUST
BE ABLE
TO IMAGINE,
EVEN A
LITTLE,
WHAT IT
WOULD FEEL
LIKE TO
LOSE HIM.

BUT
EVEN
SO...

YOU
HAVE A
BROTHER,
SO...

MY BROTHER IS *DEAD.*

...

?

...EVEN MORE OF A REASON TO FEEL SOMETHING, THEN...

AND WHAT FACE WOULD I MAKE TO SHOW THAT I DID? ONE LIKE *THAT...?*

...

WHEN MY BROTHER DIED, I DIDN'T KNOW WHAT KIND OF EXPRESSION I WAS SUPPOSED TO BE MAKING.

WELL...

SAI... I DON'T...

JERK...

...

WHIR!

WE'RE FALLING BEHIND SCHEDULE, SO EVERYONE GRAB YOUR PACKS.

ENOUGH CHIT-CHAT.

...

TRUTH BE TOLD...

...I WAS JUST ABOUT TO CLOBBER YOU AGAIN.

LUCKY YOU, SAI.

...

...I WOULDN'T HOLD BACK...

I WARNED YOU IF YOU KEPT BAD-MOUTHING SASUKE...

...THAT IN ORDER TO RESCUE SASUKE, HE'D TEAM UP WITH EVEN YOU.

THE ONLY REASON I DIDN'T KNOCK YOU INTO TOMORROW WAS BECAUSE OF WHAT NARUTO SAID...

...I CAN'T AFFORD TO HURT YOU.

FOR ONCE, HE'S BEING MORE FORGIVING THAN I AM... BUT IF YOU CAN HELP US GET OUR TEAMMATE BACK...

....?

HOW DO I SAY THIS...

...YOU'RE BEING CONSIDERATE OF HIS FEELINGS? AM I RIGHT?

SAKURA... YOU AND NARUTO...

IF WE'RE NOT IN PLACE BEFORE NOON TOMORROW, THIS MISSION IS OVER BEFORE IT EVEN STARTS.

CAN WE JUST *GO* ALREADY?

THOUGH THERE WAS SOMETHING ABOUT IT IN THIS BOOK...

I REALLY DON'T UNDERSTAND HOW SUCH FEELINGS COME ABOUT...

...

...

CRUNCH

RUSTLE

天地橋

IT'S ALMOST TIME.

(POST: TENCHI BRIDGE)

WHOO

GOOD LUCK, COM-MANDER YAMATO...

...

SASORI.

SHLEP

DREDGE

DREDGE

THAT'S ...!

TUG

...

...HOW THE TIME FLIES.

NO TAIL ...?

...YAKUSHI KABUTO...!

...

THERE REMAINS SOME DISORIENTATION FROM WHEN YOUR JUTSU DISSOLVED AND I STARTED REMEMBERING WHO I REALLY WAS...

...BUT IT'LL PASS...

HOW DO YOU FEEL?

NONE, I ASSURE YOU...

THERE ISN'T MUCH TIME, SO PLEASE BE QUICK.

I'VE RISKED MY LIFE JUST COMING HERE.

I HAVE MANY QUESTIONS.

I CAN'T BELIEVE... THE AKATSUKI SPY IS KABUTO...!

HIM AGAIN...!!

...

UCHIHA SASUKE...

...WHERE IS HE?

SOME ARE IN LANDS OUTSIDE THE SOUND...

...THAT OROCHIMARU'S SPIES HAVE INFILTRATED AND MAINTAIN FOR US.

THERE ARE SEVERAL HIDEOUTS...

...BUT THESE CHANGE FROM WEEK TO WEEK SO HIS LOCATION CANNOT BE PINPOINTED.

WHOO

UCHIHA SASUKE IS ALSO THERE RIGHT NOW.

WE'RE CURRENTLY LYING LOW AT A SAFEHOUSE ON A SMALL ISLAND IN THE NORTHERN LAKE...

...BUT WE'LL BE MOVING IN THREE DAYS' TIME.

BUT THERE IS NO SET TRANSFER PLAN OR PATTERN...

AND BEING UPWIND BLOWS OUR SCENT IN THE OPPOSITE DIRECTION, SO HE WON'T DETECT OUR APPROACH.

IDIOT! THE WIND IS EXACTLY WHAT'S KEEPING KABUTO FROM HEARING US TOO!

BLAST! THE WIND'S SO STRONG, I CAN'T HEAR A THING!

!!

WHIRL

!

HOP

POP

RUSTLE

PHEW...

...JUST A RABBIT.

TO BE CONTINUED IN *NARUTO* VOLUME 33!

IN THE NEXT VOLUME...

THE SECRET MISSION

Morphing out of control, a stronger-than-ever Naruto turns on his own teammates! Orochimaru triggers a frightening change in Naruto as he reveals a sinister plot that's been the death of far more people than anyone knew.

AVAILABLE DECEMBER 2008!
Read it first in SHONEN JUMP magazine!

You're Reading in the Wrong Direction!!

Whoops! Guess what? You're starting at the wrong end of the comic!

...It's true! In keeping with the original Japanese format, **Naruto** is meant to be read from right to left, starting in the upper-right corner.

Unlike English, which is read from left to right, Japanese is read from right to left, meaning that action, sound effects and word-balloon order are completely reversed... something which can make readers unfamiliar with Japanese feel pretty backwards themselves. For this reason, manga or Japanese comics published in the U.S. in English have sometimes been published "flopped"—that is, printed in exact reverse order, as though seen from the other side of a mirror.

By flopping pages, U.S. publishers can avoid confusing readers, but the compromise is not without its downside. For one thing, a character in a flopped manga series who once wore in the original Japanese version a T-shirt emblazoned with "M A Y" (as in "the merry month of") now wears one which reads "Y A M"! Additionally, many manga creators in Japan are themselves unhappy with the process, as some feel the mirror-imaging of their art alters their original intentions.

We are proud to bring you Masashi Kishimoto's **Naruto** in the original unflopped format. For now, though, turn to the other side of the book and let the ninjutsu begin...!

—Editor

SHONEN JUMP

NARUTO

volume 32

Naruto is a ninja-in-training with an incorrigible knack for mischief. He's got a wild sense of humor, but Naruto is completely serious about his mission to be the world's greatest ninja!

THE SEARCH FOR SASUKE

A new ninja causes trouble among the ranks of Team Kakashi when they return from the battle against Sasori. The secrets this stranger hides could be disastrous for Naruto. Meanwhile, Naruto's nemesis Orochimaru has troubles of his own—his stronghold may be infiltrated by a spy!

The smash-hit manga that's sold more than 3.6 million books in the U.S.A.!!

www.shonenjump.com

$7.95 USA $9.50 CAN £5.99 UK

ISBN-13: 978-1-4215-1944-9
ISBN-10:   1-4215-1944-5

50795

**This book reads
from right to left.**

media

RATED
T
FOR
TEEN
ratings.viz.com

9 781421 519449